Graphic Organisers

for

Reading

Brilliant
PUBLICATIONS

Kathleen Bullock, Cherrie Farnette,
Marjorie Frank,
Jill Norris and Kris Sexton

We hope you and your pupils enjoy using the ideas in this book. Brilliant Publications publishes many other books to help primary school teachers. To find out more details on all of our titles, including those listed below, please go to our website: www.brilliantpublications.co.uk.

Other books you may be interested in:
Graphic Organisers for Writing   978-0-85747-438-4
Graphic Organisers for Any Subject   978-0-85747-439-1

Published by Brilliant Publications
Unit 10
Sparrow Hall Farm
Edlesborough
Dunstable
Bedfordshire
LU6 2ES, UK

Email: info@brilliantpublications.co.uk
Website: www.brilliantpublications.co.uk
Tel: 01525 222292

The name Brilliant Publications and the logo are registered trademarks.

Written by Kathleen Bullock, Cherrie Farnette, Marjorie Frank, Jill Norris and Kris Sexton.

© 2006 Incentive Publications Inc.

Published in the UK by Brilliant Publications with permission from Incentive Publications Inc.

Printed ISBN 978-0-85747-437-7
E-pdf ISBN 978-0-85747-807-8

First printed and published in the UK in 2015
10 9   8   7   6   5   4   3   2   1

The right of Kathleen Bullock, Cherrie Farnette, Marjorie Frank, Jill Norris and Kris Sexton to be identified as the authors of this work has been asserted by themselves in accordance with the Copyright, Designs and Patents Act 1988.

Contents

Introduction

Research in many subject areas shows that using graphic organisers, or writing frames as they are sometimes known, leads to improved pupil performance on assessments and enhanced critical thinking skills. Such tools help pupils to think about the way they think and learn, and how to best display their ideas showing their level of understanding. Organising visually is a way to process, analyse and synthesise ideas so as to understand them more deeply.

Pupils who plan and write with graphic organisers generate more ideas, recall and analyse data, recognise relationships between concepts and relate new ideas to previous knowledge and real life.

Graphic Organisers for Reading contains 60 graphic organisers for fiction and non-fiction action, literary elements and genre and reading in any content area. The organisers can be used to reinforce important reading strategies.

Character Wheel

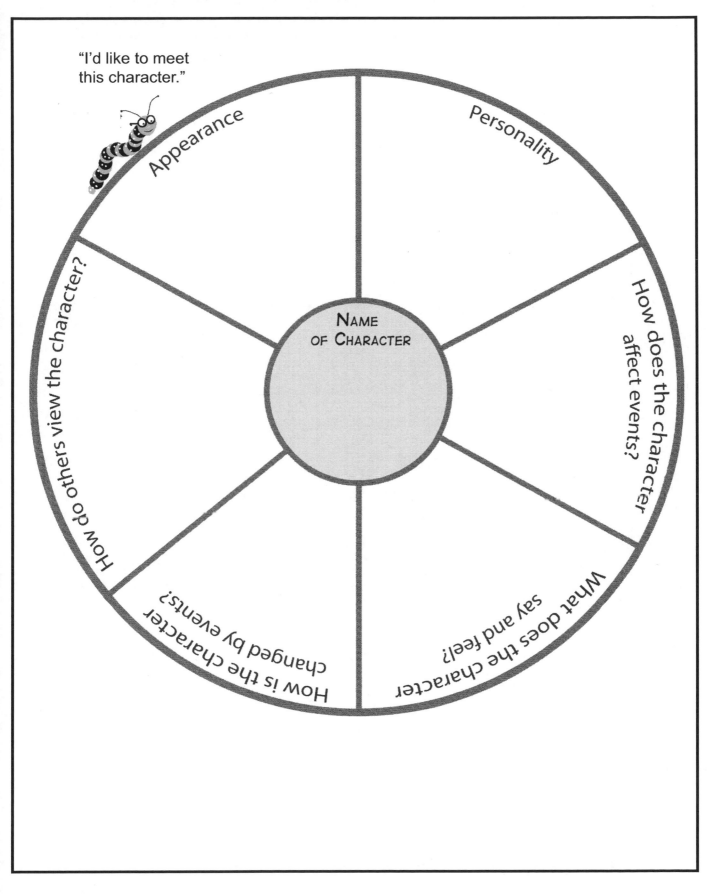

"I'd like to meet this character."

Appearance

Personality

How does the character affect events?

How do others view the character?

NAME OF CHARACTER

How is the character changed by events?

What does the character say and feel?

Name: _____

Short Story Guide

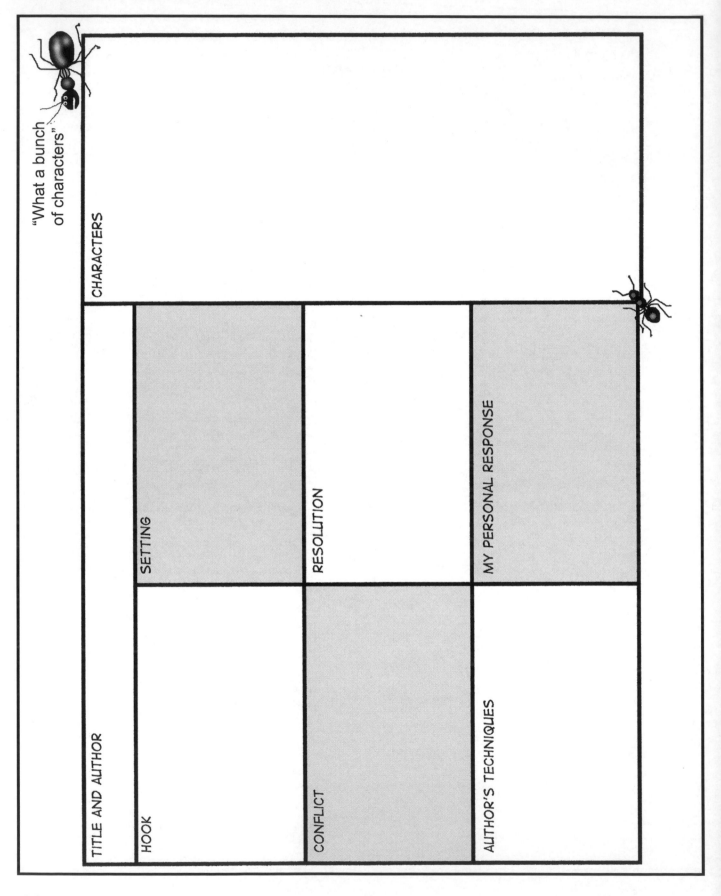

"What a bunch of characters"

CHARACTERS

TITLE AND AUTHOR

SETTING

HOOK

RESOLUTION

CONFLICT

MY PERSONAL RESPONSE

AUTHOR'S TECHNIQUES

Name: _____

Published by Brilliant Publications

Story Map

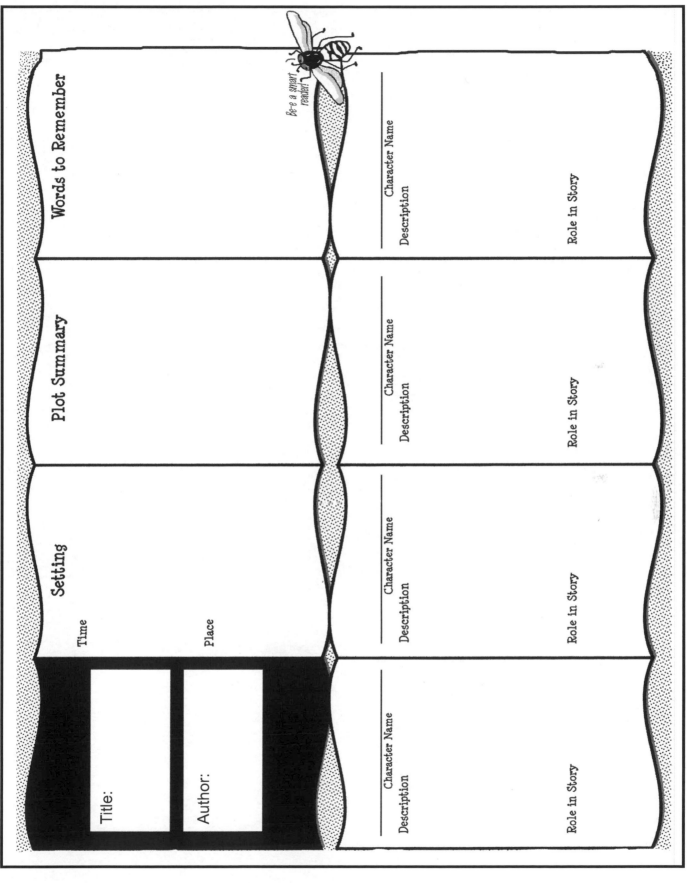

Words to Remember

Plot Summary

Setting

Time

Place

Title:

Author:

Character Name

Description

Role in Story

Character Name

Description

Role in Story

Character Name

Description

Role in Story

Character Name

Description

Role in Story

be-e a smart reader!

Name: _____

Storyline

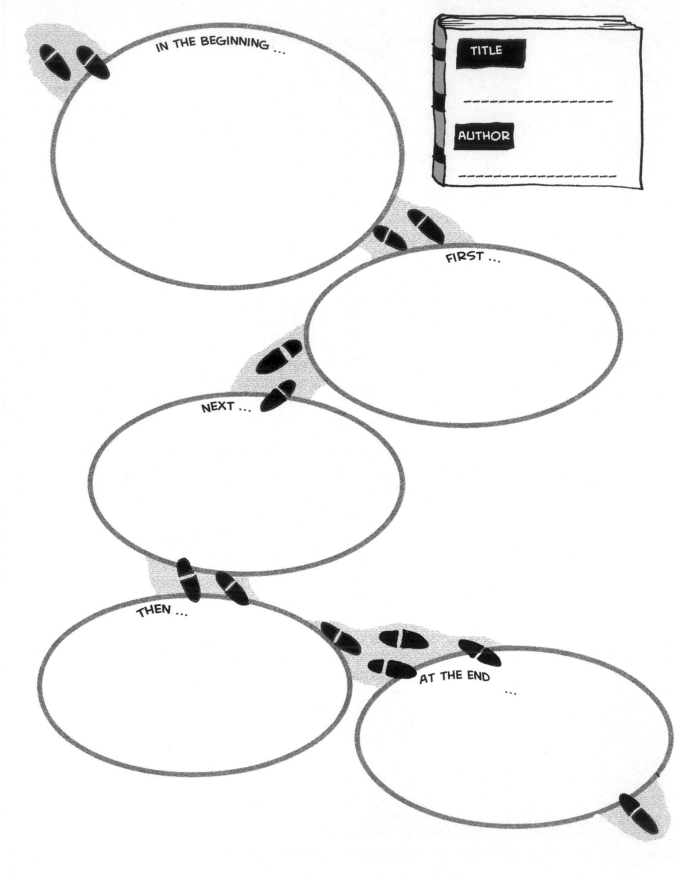

IN THE BEGINNING ...

TITLE

AUTHOR

FIRST ...

NEXT ...

THEN ...

AT THE END ...

Name: _____

Plot Links

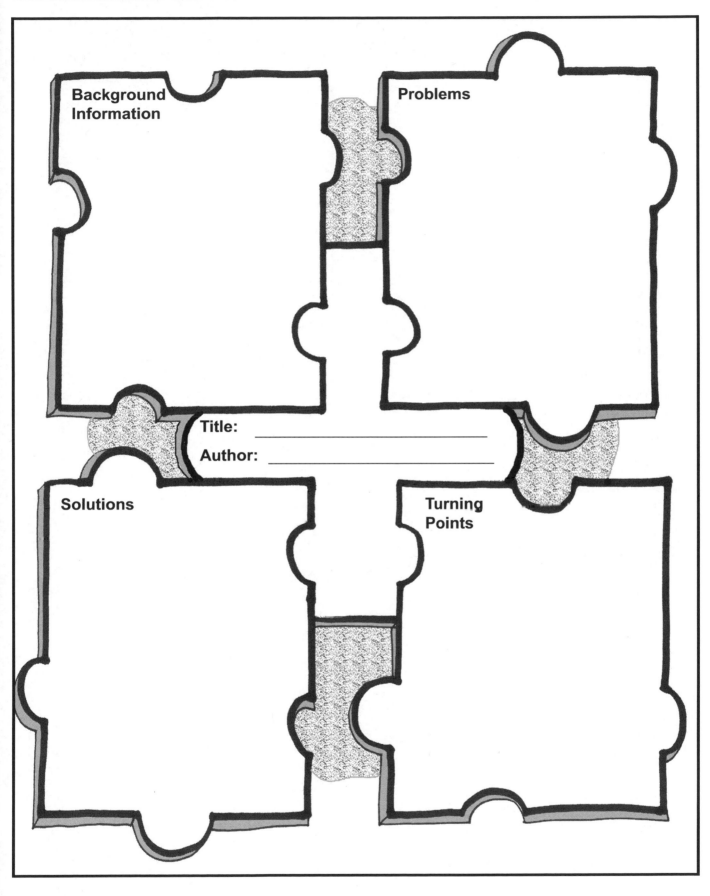

Background
Information

Problems

Title: _____

Author: _____

Solutions

Turning
Points

Name: _____

A Staircase of Events

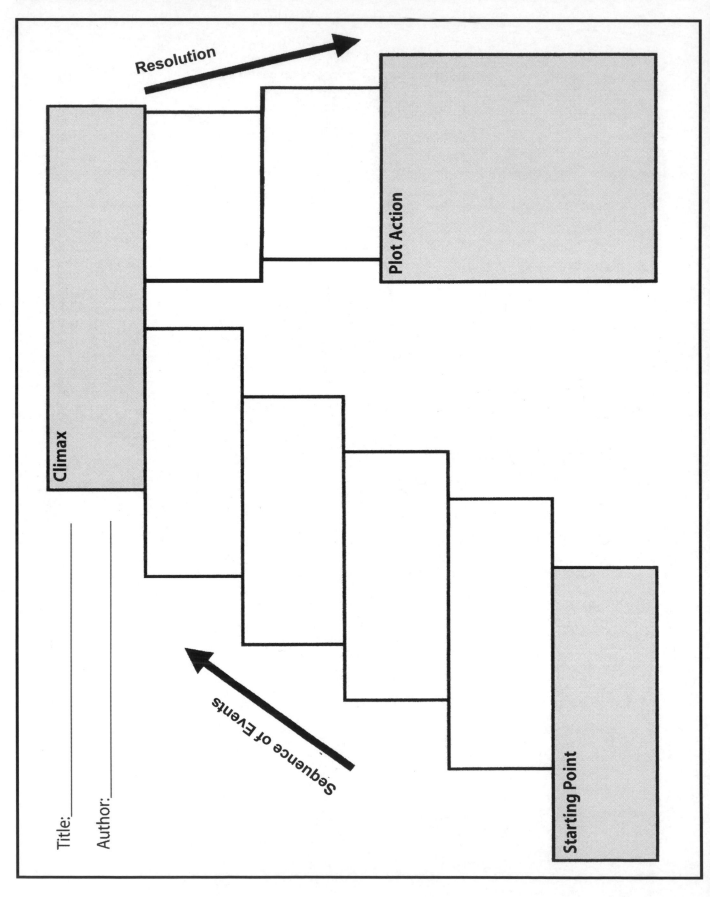

Name: _____

Setting

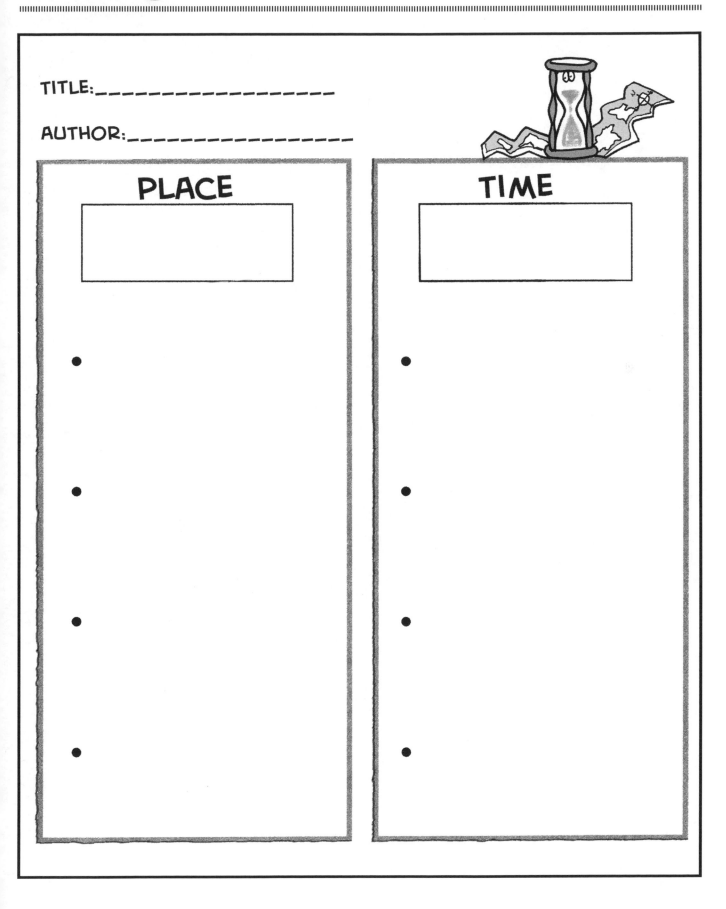

TITLE:_ _ _ _ _ _ _ _ _ _ _ _ _ _ _ _

AUTHOR:_ _ _ _ _ _ _ _ _ _ _ _ _ _

PLACE

-
-
-
-

TIME

-
-
-
-

Name: _____

Word Net

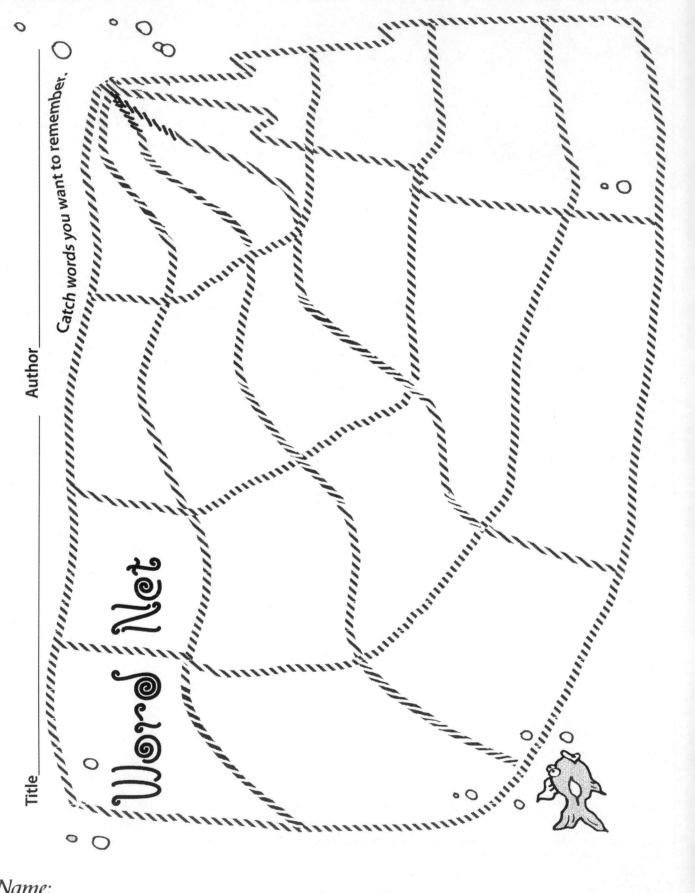

Title

Author

Catch words you want to remember.

Word Net

Name: _____

Mood

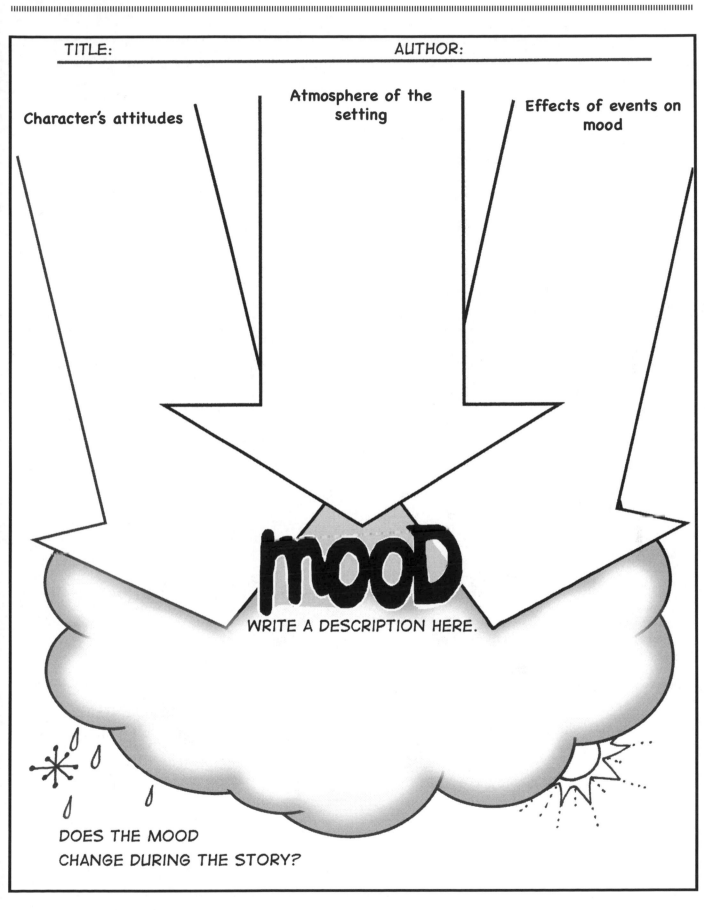

TITLE: _____ AUTHOR: _____

Character's attitudes

Atmosphere of the setting

Effects of events on mood

mood

WRITE A DESCRIPTION HERE.

DOES THE MOOD
CHANGE DURING THE STORY?

Name: _____

What is the Storyteller's Role?

Title:_____   Author:_____

Storyteller: _____

☐ **All-Knowing Observer -**
An outside voice understands all the character's emotions and tells the story.

☐ **Objective Reporter -**
A detached observer reports the facts.

☐ **First Person -**
A character tells the story from a personal point of view.

☐ **Third Person -**
An outside voice tells and comments on characters and the story.

Give examples that support your answer.

Example

Example

Example

How does the point of view affect your response to this story?_____

_____

_____

_____

Name: _____

This page may be photocopied for use by the purchasing institution only.
Published by Brilliant Publications

Author's Toolbox

PERSONIFICATION

EXPLICIT VERBS

SIMILES

ALLITERATION

METAPHORS

PICTURE LANGUAGE

MY REACTION:

TITLE_____

AUTHOR_____

Name: _____

Actions and Reactions

Title_____ Author_____

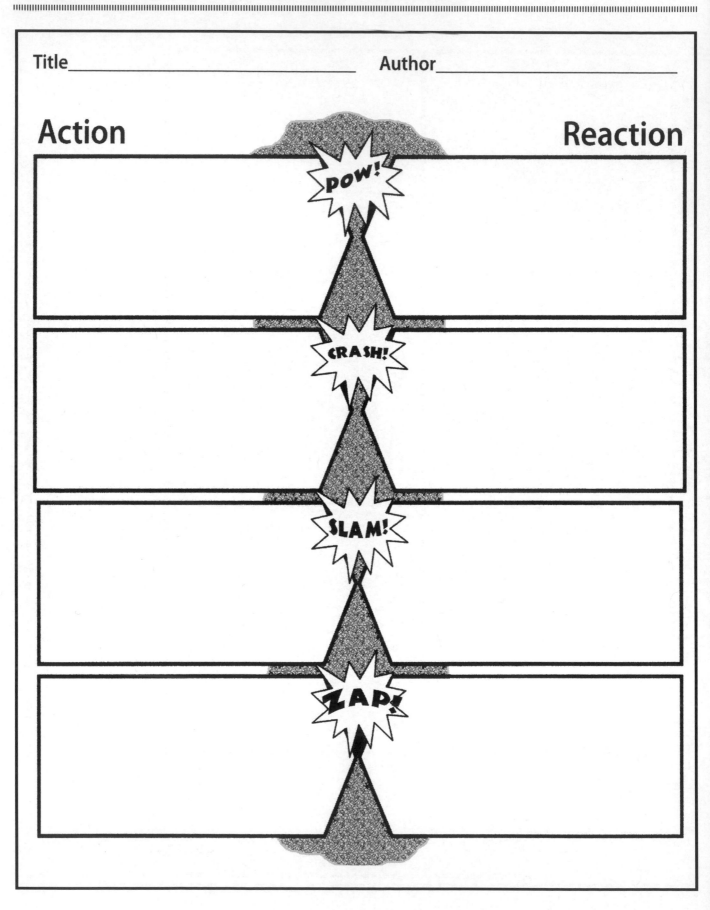

Action

Reaction

POW!

CRASH!

SLAM!

ZAP!

Name: _____

This page may be photocopied for use by the purchasing institution only.
Published by Brilliant Publications

Personal Connections

It happened to_____
(character's name)

in_____.
(title)

It happened here_____.
(setting)

This is what happened:

It happened to me when I was_____.
(age)

It happened to me here_____.
(setting)

This is what happened:

Name: _____

Published by Brilliant Publications

Character Squares

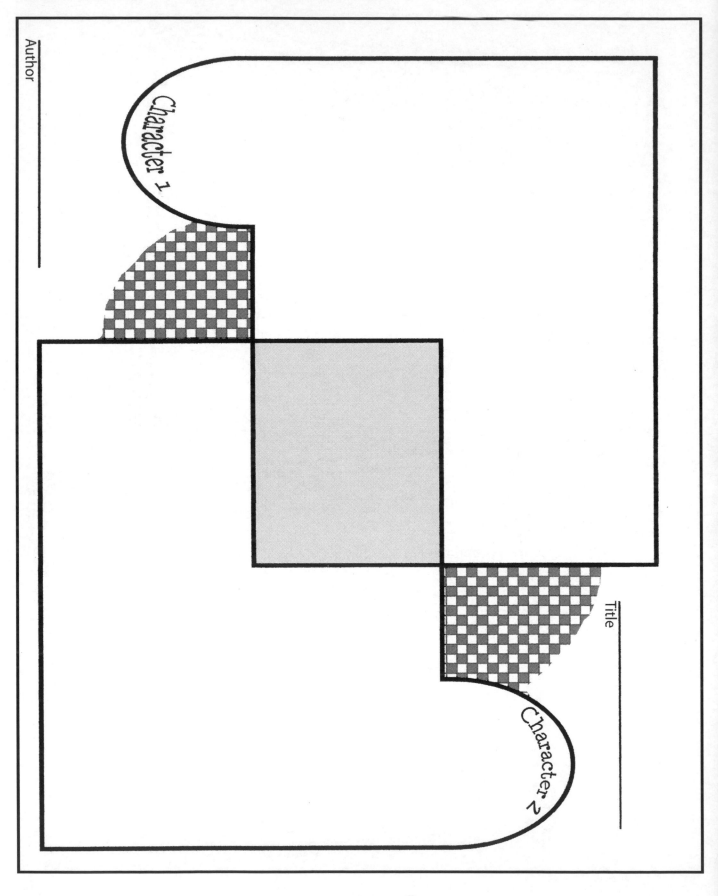

Character 1

Title

Character 2

Name: _____

Good versus Evil

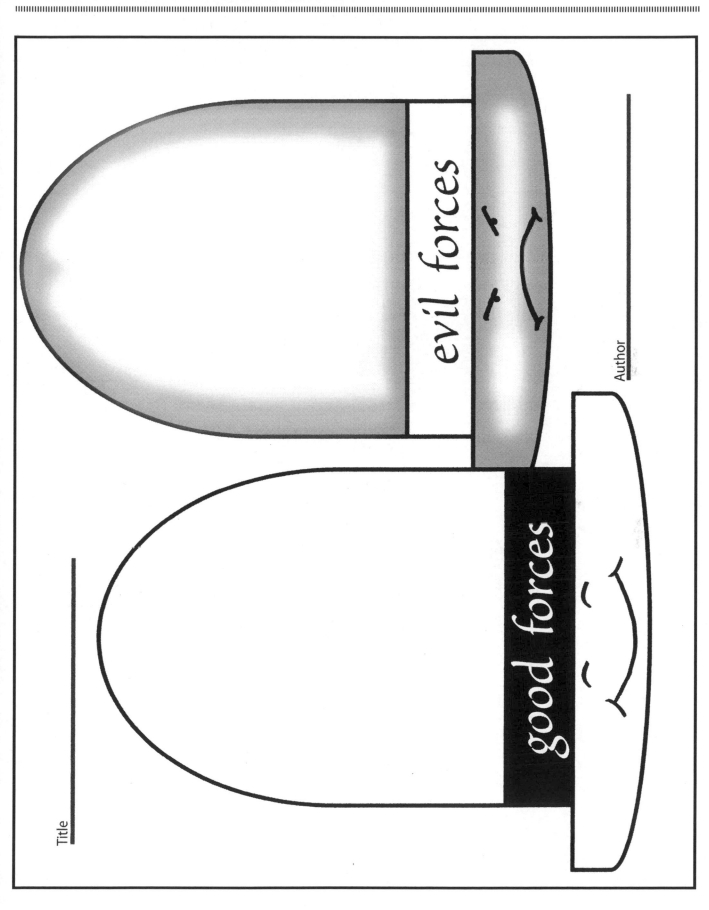

evil forces

Author _____

good forces

Title _____

Name: _____

Making Predictions

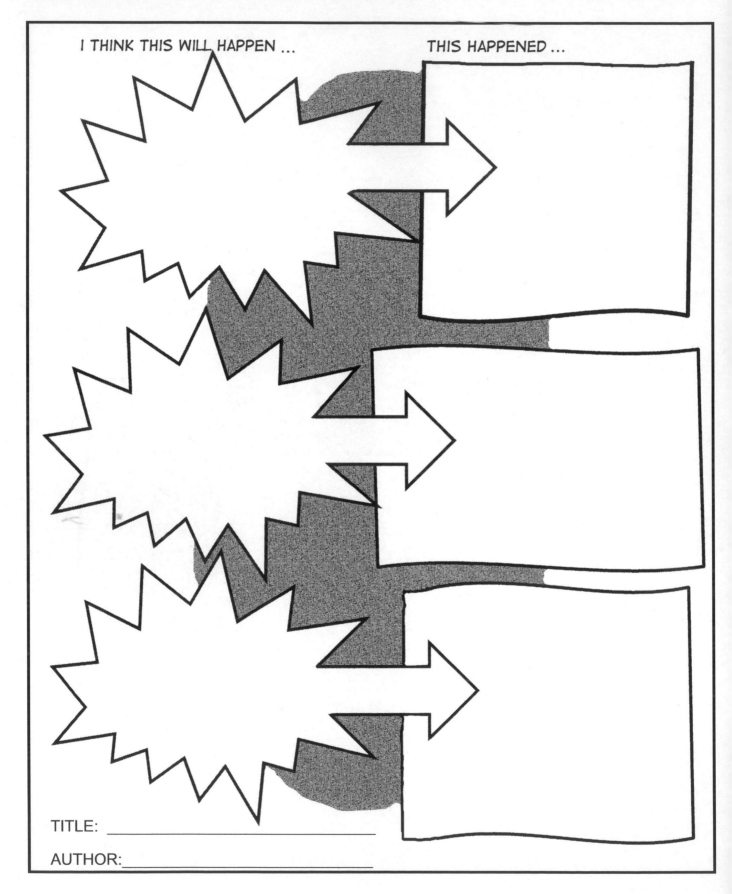

I THINK THIS WILL HAPPEN ...

THIS HAPPENED ...

TITLE: _____

AUTHOR: _____

Name: _____

Published by Brilliant Publications

Thinking About the Author

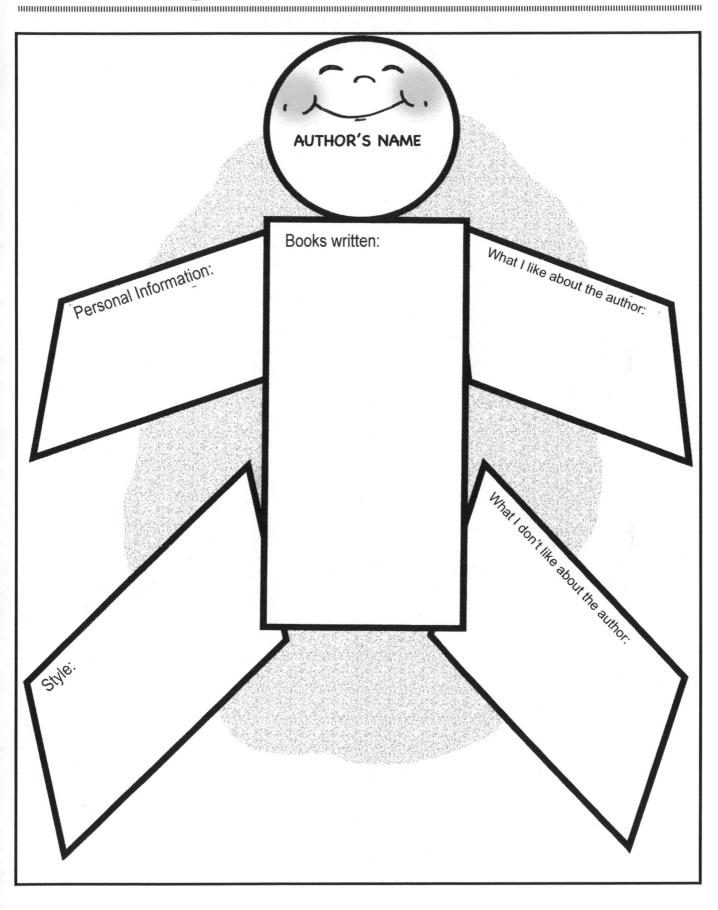

AUTHOR'S NAME

Books written:

Personal Information:

What I like about the author:

What I don't like about the author:

Style:

Name: _____

Published by Brilliant Publications

Thinking About the Illustrator

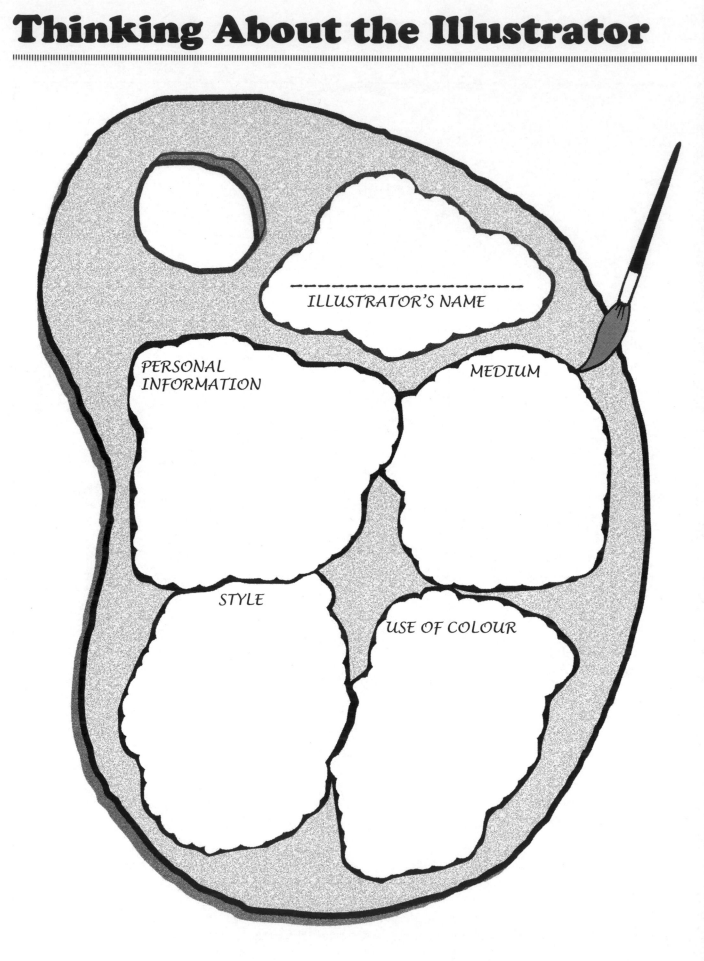

ILLUSTRATOR'S NAME

PERSONAL
INFORMATION

MEDIUM

STYLE

USE OF COLOUR

Name: _____

Published by Brilliant Publications

Identifying Cause and Effect

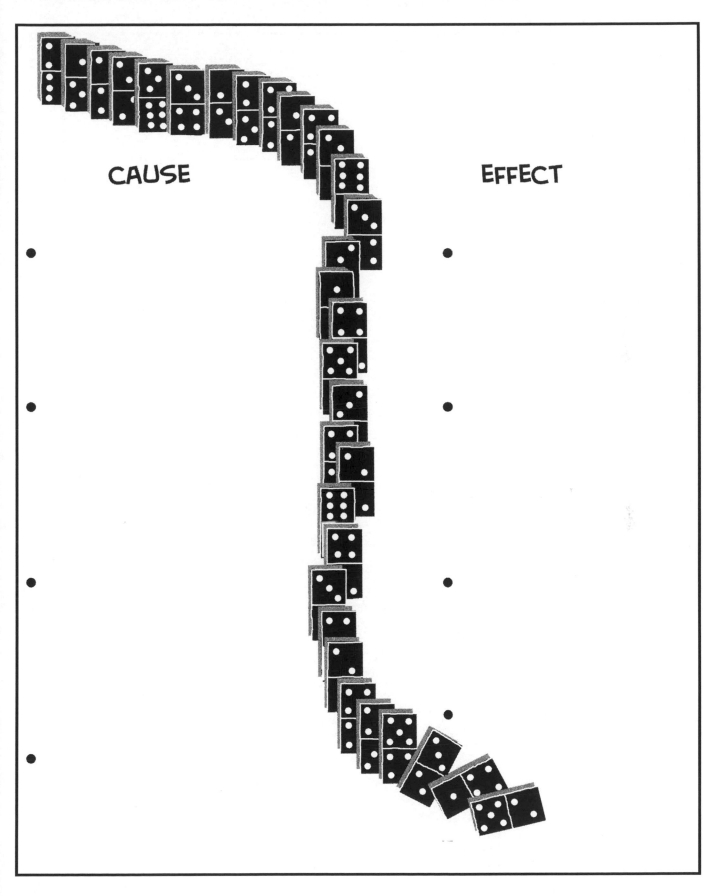

CAUSE

EFFECT

Name: _____

Follow the Clues

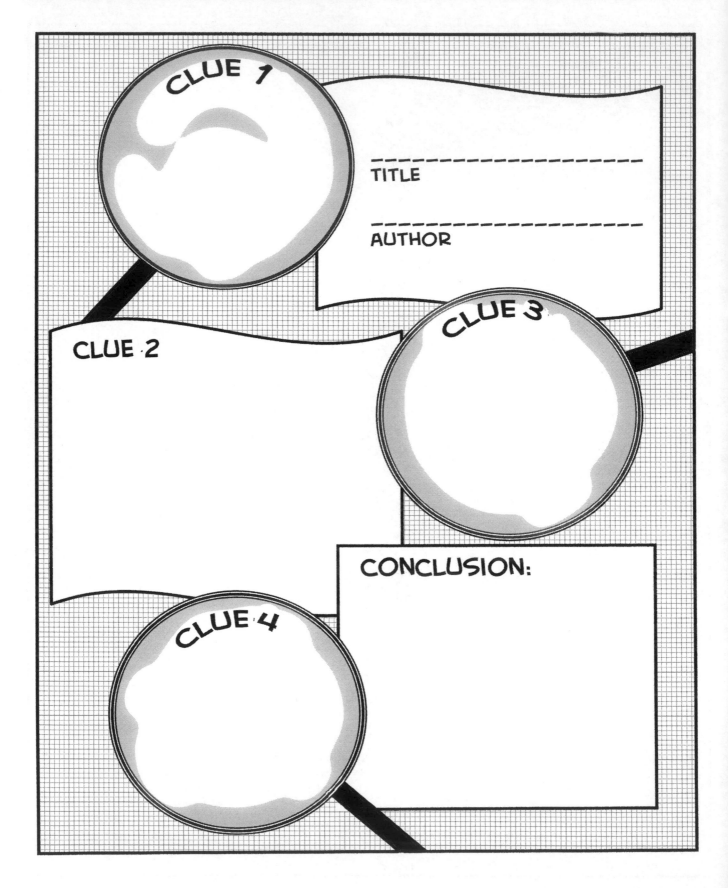

CLUE 1

TITLE _____

AUTHOR _____

CLUE 2

CLUE 3

CONCLUSION:

CLUE 4

Name: _____

Understanding Symbols

THE SYMBOLS

Symbols are concrete objects that stand for an idea.

"In literature, ladybirds are symbols of mother love."

WHAT THEY MEAN

Give an example from the story.

"Some authors use the bee as a symbol of industriousness."

Title _____

Author _____

Name: _____

Nonfiction Reading Guide

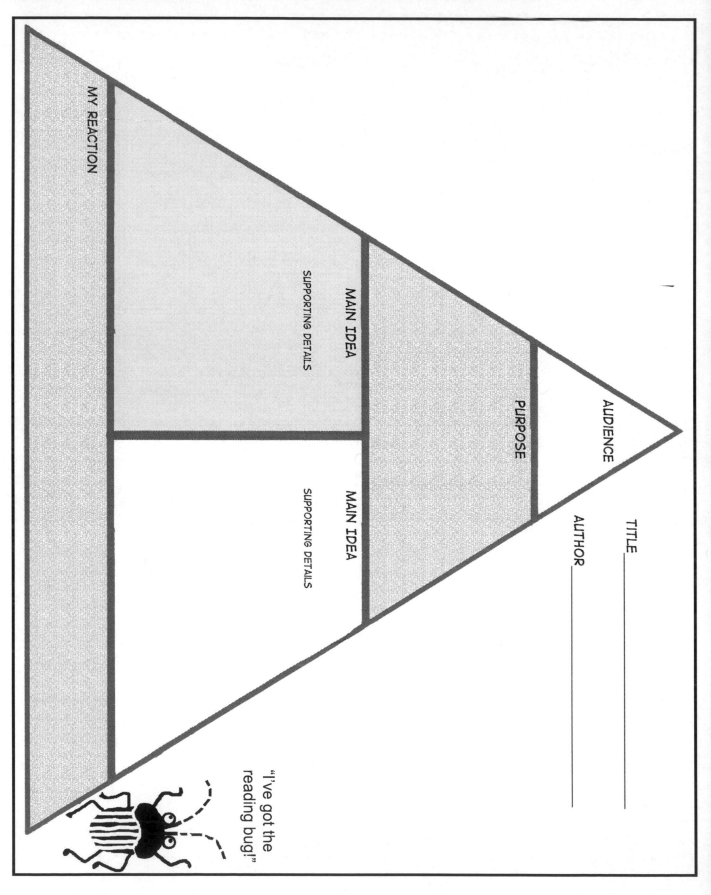

MY REACTION

SUPPORTING DETAILS

MAIN IDEA

SUPPORTING DETAILS

MAIN IDEA

PURPOSE

AUDIENCE

AUTHOR _____

TITLE _____

"I've got the reading bug!"

Name: _____

Published by Brilliant Publications

Main Idea and Details

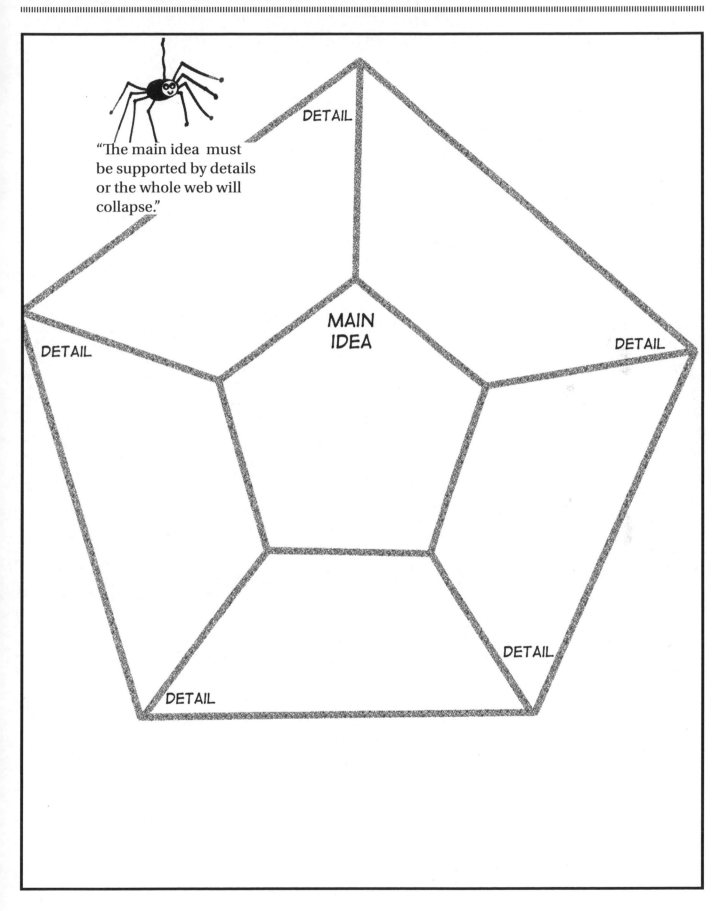

"The main idea must be supported by details or the whole web will collapse."

DETAIL

DETAIL

DETAIL

MAIN IDEA

DETAIL

DETAIL

Name: _____

Reading About History

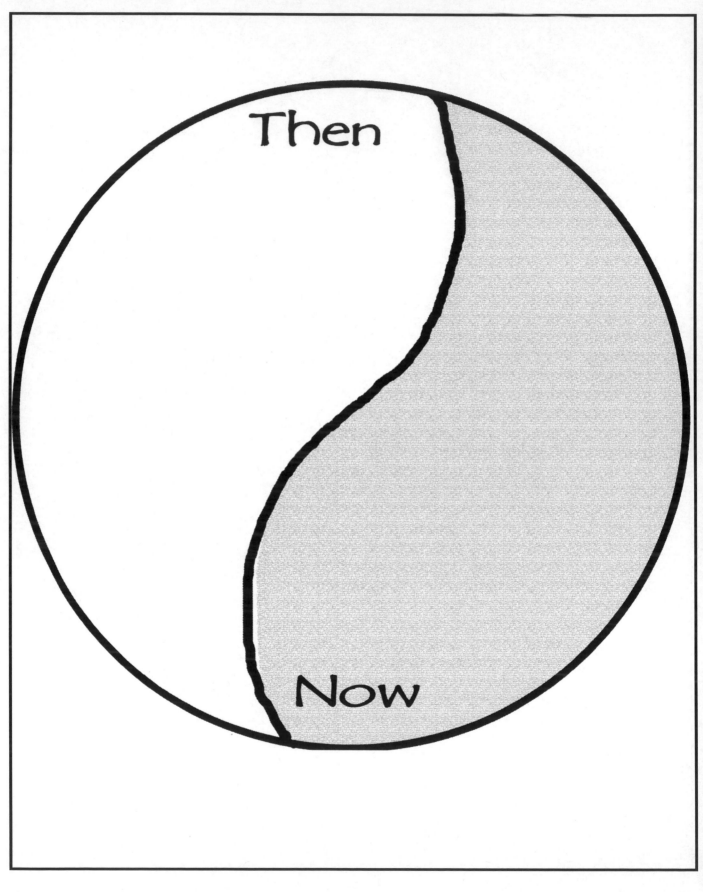

Name: _____

Fact Finder

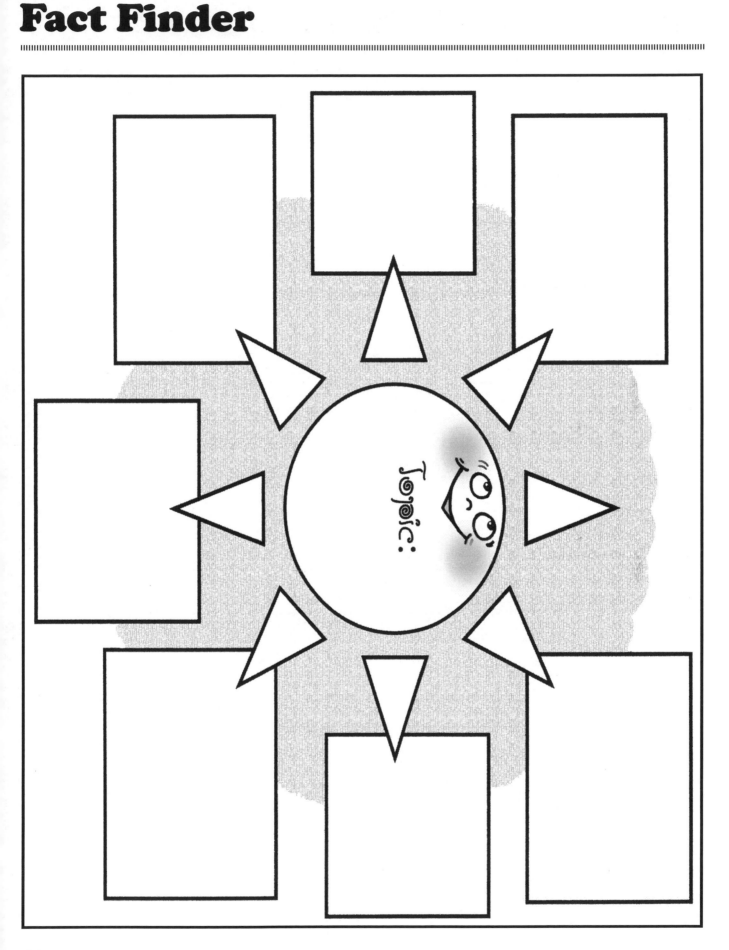

Name: _____

As I Read, I'll Think About It ...

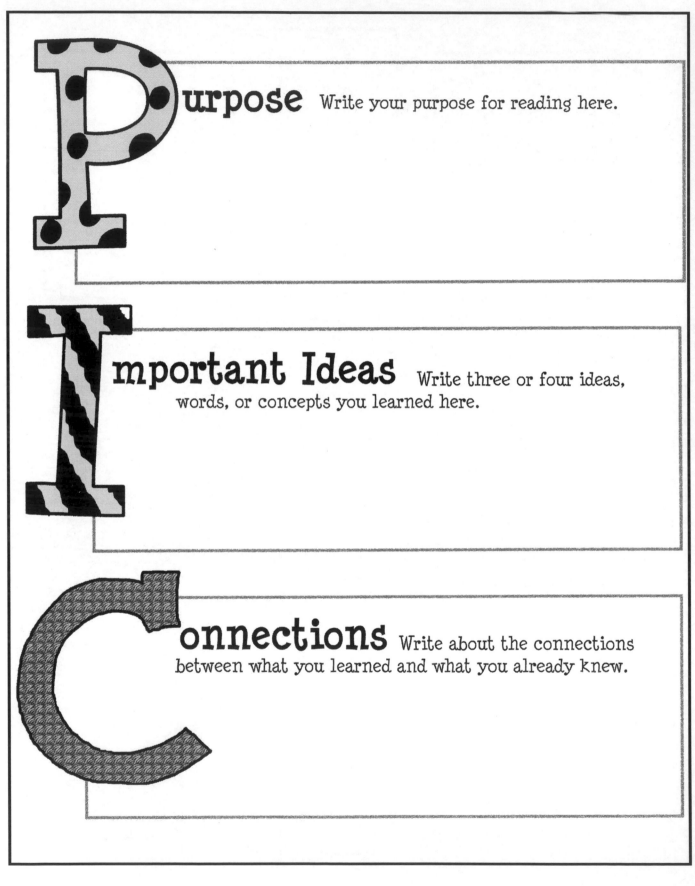

Purpose   Write your purpose for reading here.

Important Ideas   Write three or four ideas, words, or concepts you learned here.

Connections   Write about the connections between what you learned and what you already knew.

Name: _____

Published by Brilliant Publications

Reading Survey

1. LOOK AT THE TITLE. ☐
2. READ THE INSTRUCTIONS. ☐
3. READ THE MAIN HEADINGS. ☐
4. READ THE FIRST AND LAST PARAGRAPHS. ☐
5. READ THE SUMMARY.
   WRITE A SUMMARY IN YOUR OWN WORDS.

_____

_____

_____

_____

_____

_____

6. IDENTIFY THE SOURCE.

_____

Name: _____

KWL

"I am **K**een, **W**ise and **L**iterate."

WHAT I KNOW **K**	WHAT I WANT TO KNOW **W**	WHAT I LEARNED **L**
BEFORE READING	BEFORE READING	AFTER READING

Name: _____

KWHL

"A wise owl **K**nows **W**hat and **H**ow to **L**earn."

WHAT I **K**NOW	WHAT I **W**ANT TO KNOW	**H**OW I CAN FIND THE INFORMATION	WHAT I **L**EARNED
BEFORE READING	BEFORE READING	DURING READING	AFTER READING

Name: _____

Reading the Visuals

Selection Read:_____ Author:_____

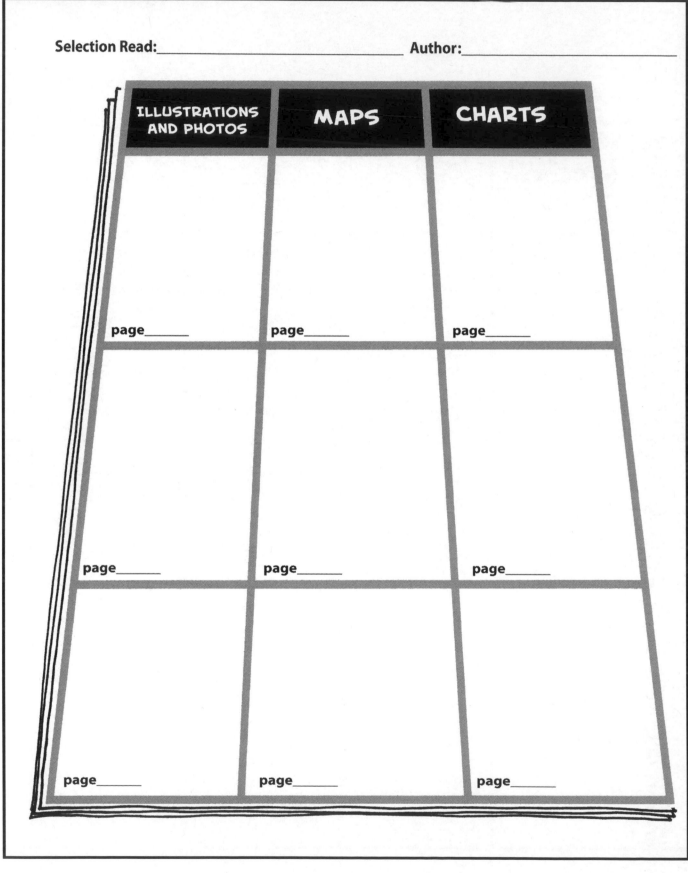

ILLUSTRATIONS AND PHOTOS	MAPS	CHARTS
page_____	page_____	page_____
page_____	page_____	page_____
page_____	page_____	page_____

Name: _____

This page may be photocopied for use by the purchasing institution only.
Published by Brilliant Publications

Research Map

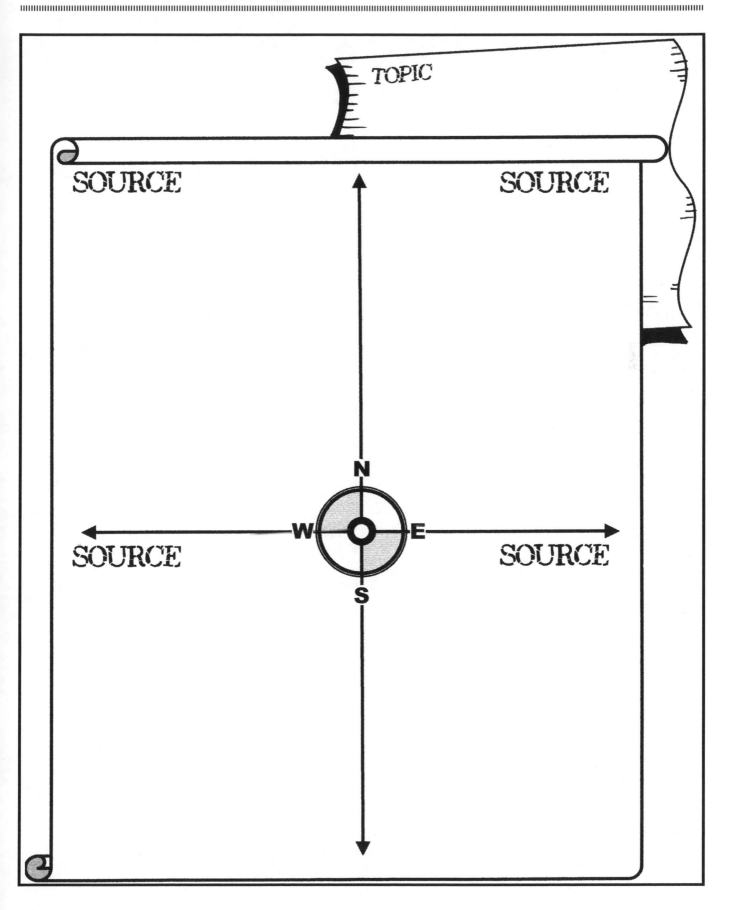

TOPIC

SOURCE

SOURCE

N

W · E

S

SOURCE

SOURCE

Name: _____

Chapter Map Study Guide

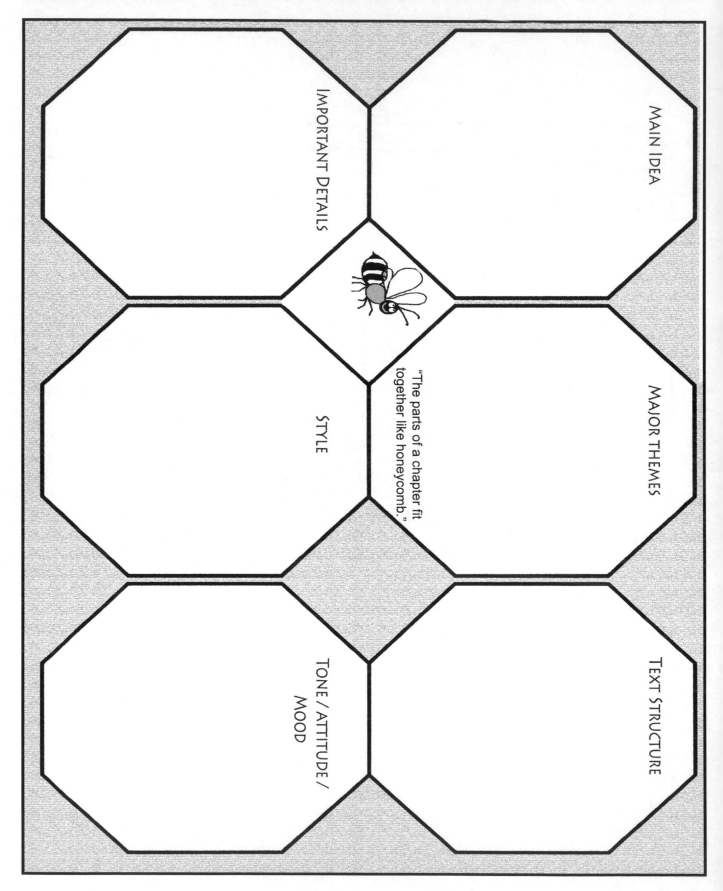

IMPORTANT DETAILS

MAIN IDEA

STYLE

"The parts of a chapter fit together like honeycomb."

MAJOR THEMES

TONE / ATTITUDE / MOOD

TEXT STRUCTURE

Name: _____

Published by Brilliant Publications

Signal Words

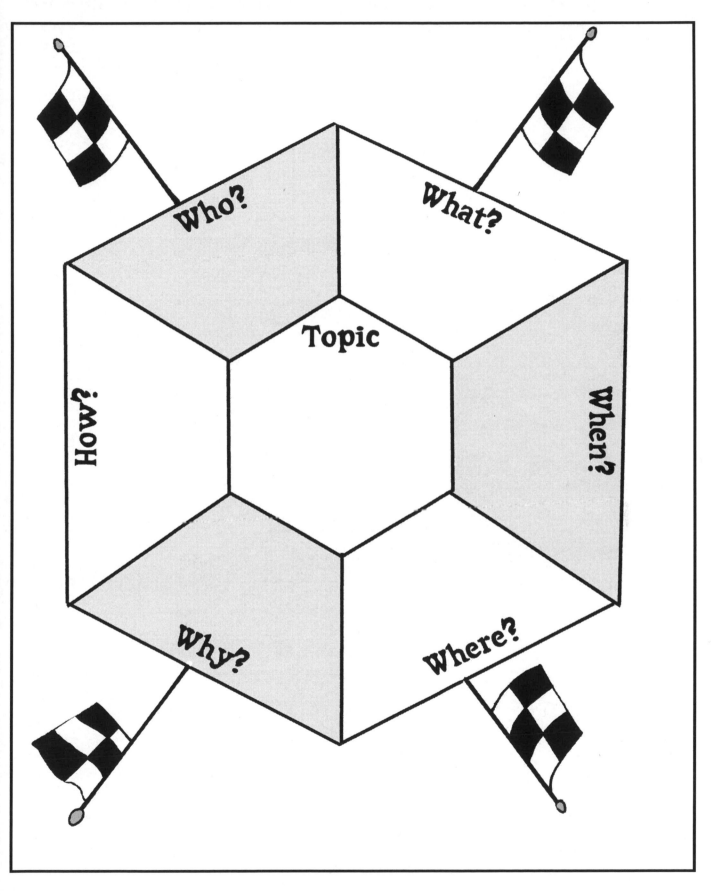

Name: _____

Comparing Two Stories

STORY 1: _____

STORY 2: _____

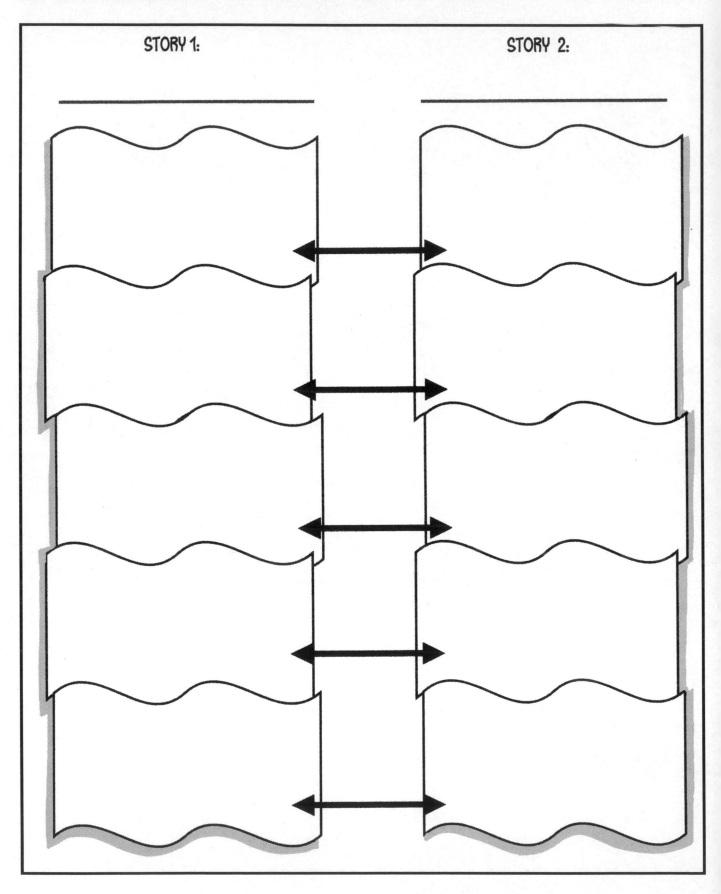

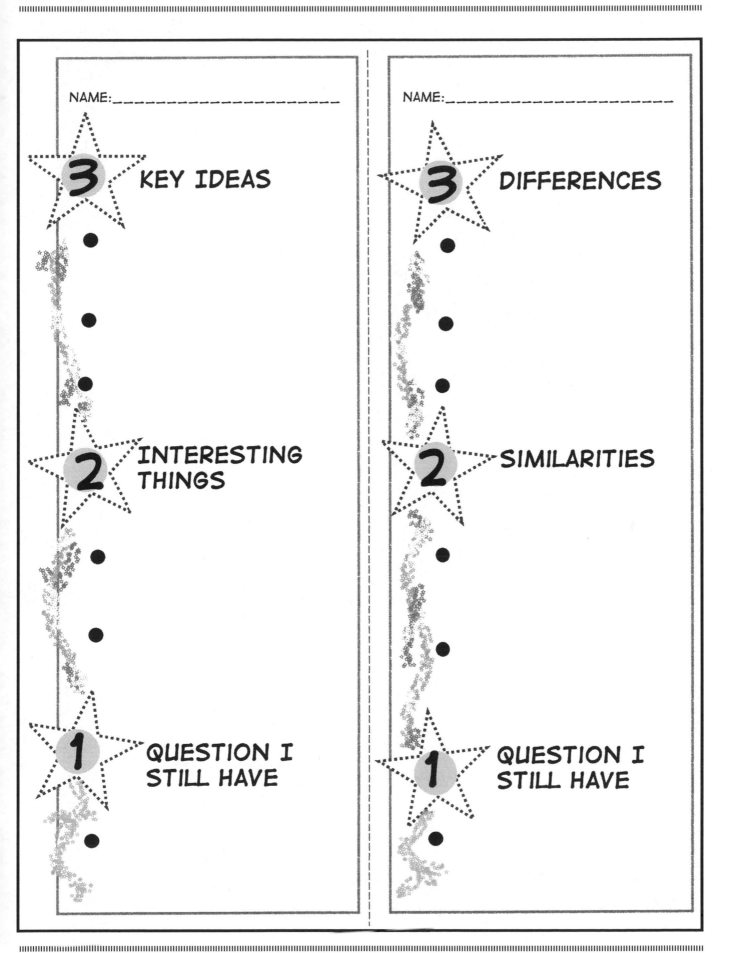

NAME:_____

3 KEY IDEAS

-
-
-

2 INTERESTING THINGS

-
-

1 QUESTION I STILL HAVE

-

NAME:_____

3 DIFFERENCES

-
-
-

2 SIMILARITIES

-
-

1 QUESTION I STILL HAVE

-

The End!

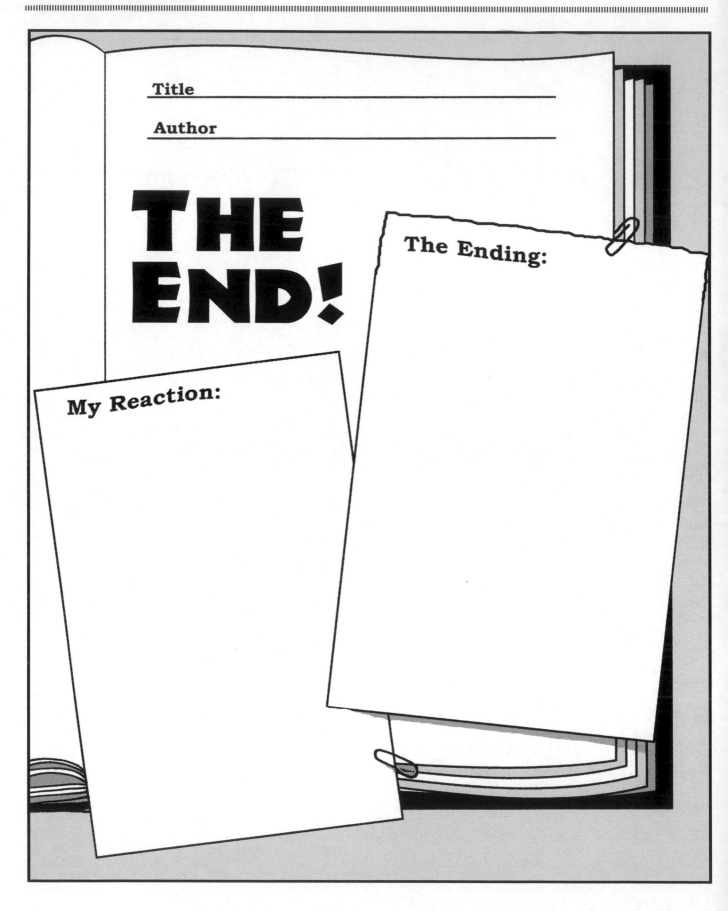

Title _____

Author _____

THE END!

The Ending:

My Reaction:

Name: _____

This page may be photocopied for use by the purchasing institution only.
Published by Brilliant Publications

Give Me Five (+ One)

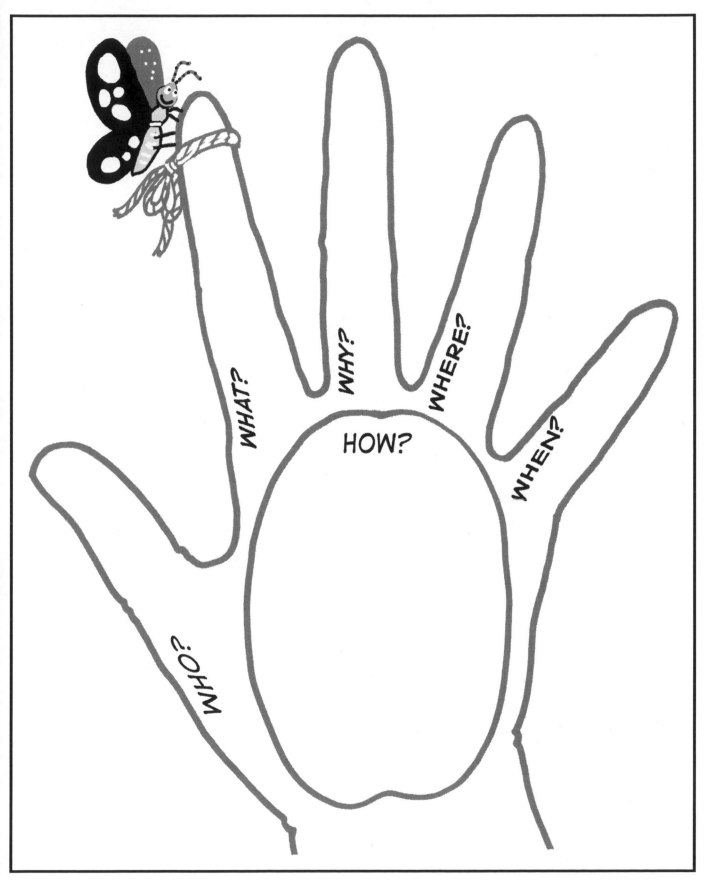

Name: _____

Mysteries

Important mystery in story:

Attributes of Mysteries:

- ☐ Problem or crime to solve
- ☐ Protagonist solves the mystery
- ☐ Clues are provided
- ☐ A wrongdoer is revealed
- ☐ Innocent suspects

Clues to its solution:

Solution:

Were you surprised?

Why or why not?

Name: _____

Poetry

The subject of the poem:

Attributes of Poetry:

- ☐ A few powerful words
- ☐ Strong images or emotions
- ☐ Made-up words or phrases
- ☐ Rhyme or rhythm
- ☐ Repetition or pattern

What it says to me:

Examples of elements

Rhyme	Images
Rhythm	Words

Name: _____

Realistic Fiction

Setting:

Characters:

Name   Role in story

Attributes of Realistic Fiction:

☐ Story or events could really happen

☐ The characters seem real

☐ The setting seems real

☐ The details seem real

☐ I learn about myself and others as I read

Story events:

Real events:

Name: _____

Science Fiction

Setting:

Characters:

Name   Role in story

Attributes of Science Fiction:

☐ The action takes place in the future or in another dimension

☐ The premise of the story is scientifically imaginable

☐ There is some travel through space

☐ Robots or aliens are characters in the story

Impossible events:

Name: _____

Biographies

Subject:

Description:

Contributions:

Attributes of Biographies:

☐ Story about a real person

☐ Gives facts about where and when that person lived

☐ Explains what that person is remembered for

☐ Tells of important events in that person's life.

Interesting facts:

A question you would ask:

Name: _____

Published by Brilliant Publications

Animal Stories

Setting:

Characters:

Name   Role in story

Attributes of Animal Stories:

☐   The main characters are animals

☐   The animals are realistic

☐   The animals are imaginary

Realistic elements:

Fictional elements:

Name: _____

Fables

Characters:

Attributes of Fables:

☐ The purpose of the story is to teach a lesson

☐ There is a moral at the end

☐ The story is short

Action:

Lessons taught:

Moral:

Name: _____

Fairy Tales

Setting:

Good characters:

Bad/evil characters:

Attributes of Fairy Tales:

- ☐ Good characters versus evil ones
- ☐ Royalty and/or castle
- ☐ Special beginning and ending:
  Once upon a time …
  And they all lived happily ever after.
- ☐ Magic involved somewhere
- ☐ Problem and solution
- ☐ Things happen in threes or sevens.

Magic:

Summary of story:

Name: _____

Fantasy

Setting:

Characters:

Attributes of Fantasy:

☐ The story setting is not realistic

☐ Story elements are make-believe

☐ The events could not happen in reality

☐ The animals or 'things' talk

Elements of fantasy:

Name: _____

Historical Fiction

Setting:

Characters:

Attributes of Historical Fiction:

☐ The setting represents a real time

☐ The setting represents a real place

☐ The characters in the story are real people

☐ The story is about actual historical events

Summary of Action:

Historical significance:

Name: _____

Humour

Characters:

Funny events:

Attributes of Humour

☐ The dialogue made me smile or laugh

☐ The characters made me smile or laugh

☐ The events made me smile or laugh

What makes it funny?

Name: _____

Double Venn

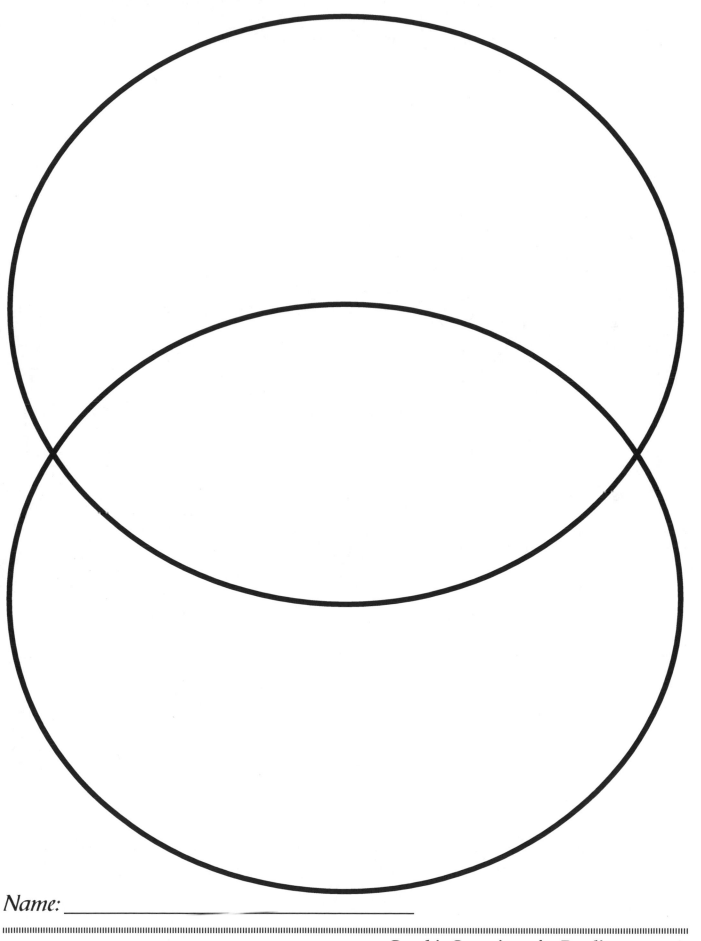

Name: _____

Triple Venn

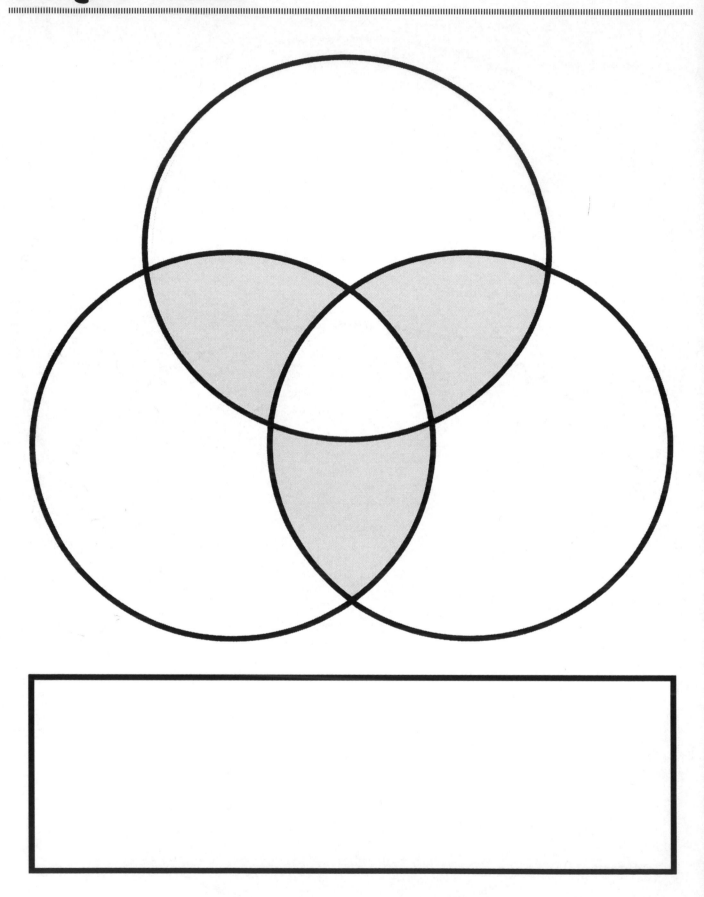

Wheel

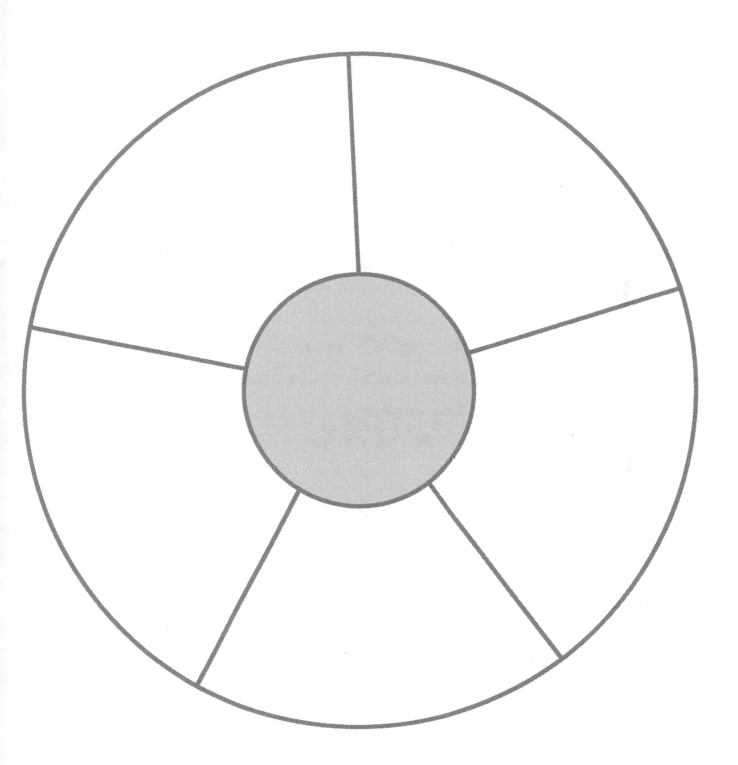

Name: _____

||||||||||||||||||||||||||||||||||||||||||||||||||||||||||||||||||||||||||||||||||||||||||||||||||||||||||||||||||||||||||||||

This page may be photocopied for use by the purchasing institution only.   **Graphic Organisers for Reading**   **55**
Published by Brilliant Publications

Cluster

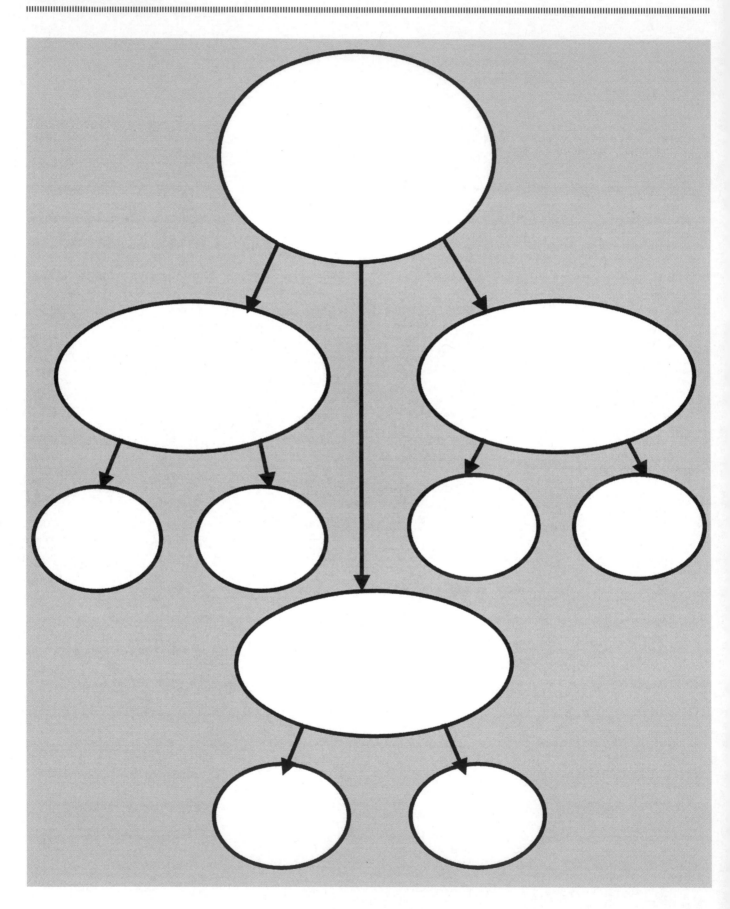

Name: _____

Two-column Table

Name: _____

Three-column Table

Name: _____

Four-column Table

Name: _____

Bow Tie

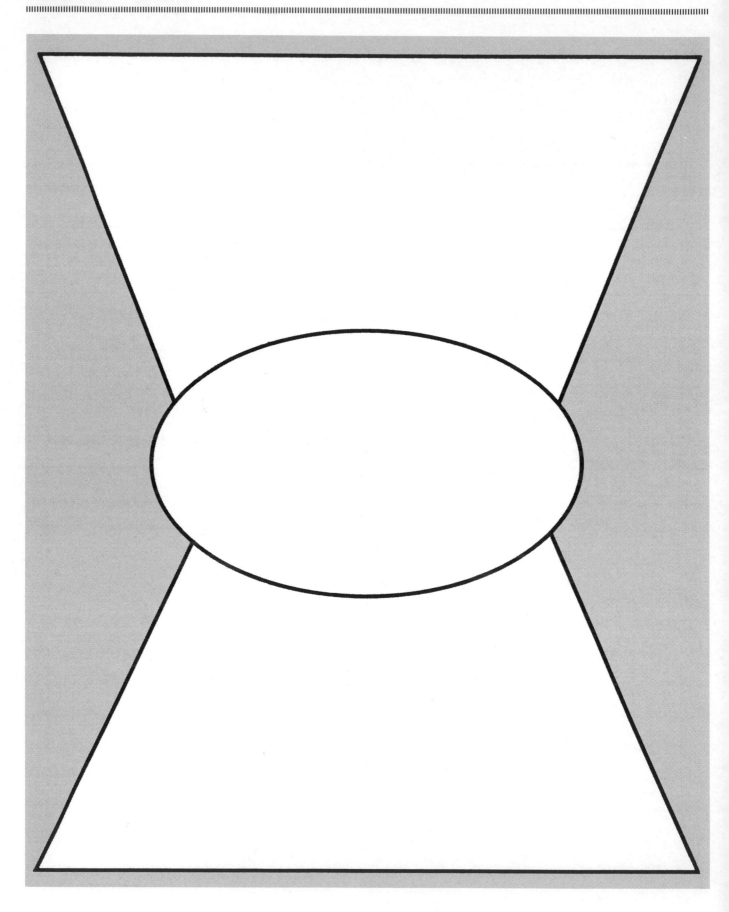

Name: _____

This page may be photocopied for use by the purchasing institution only.
Published by Brilliant Publications

Circle-ray

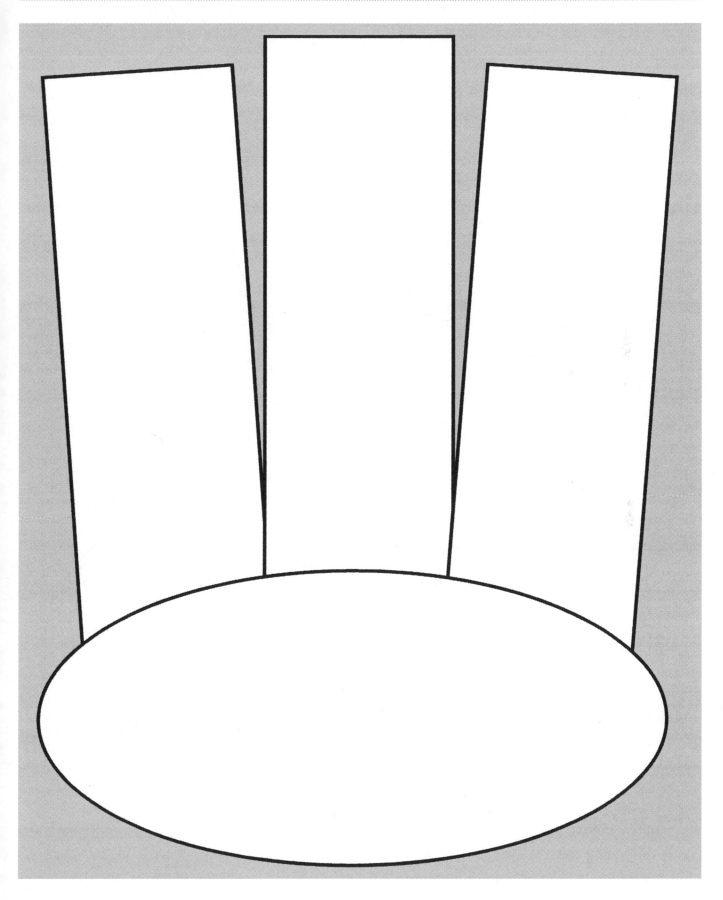

Name: _____

Hand

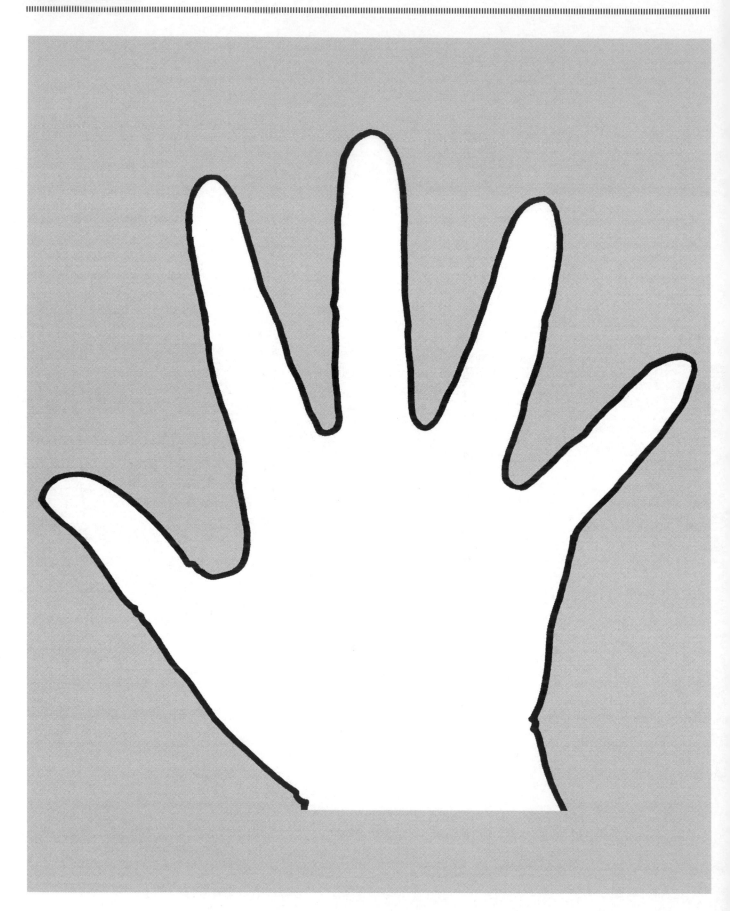

Name: _____

This page may be photocopied for use by the purchasing institution only.
Published by Brilliant Publications

Star

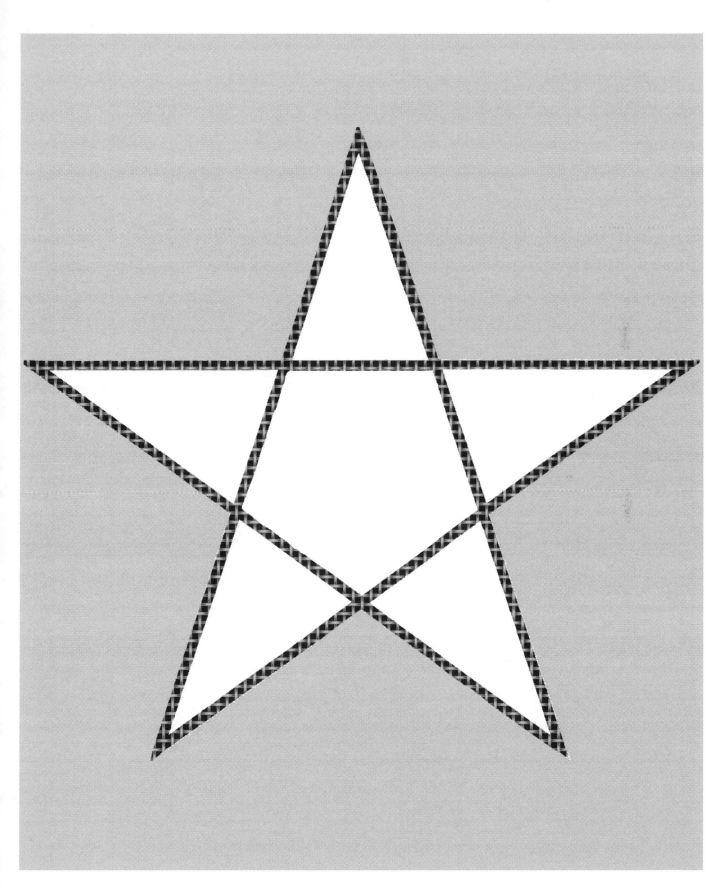

Name: _____